Stories for Children

By
Shaykh Mufti Saiful Islām

JKN Publications

First Published in December 2014 - 3000 copies
Second Edition - October 2017 - 3000 copies
Third Edition - December 2021 - 5000 copies

ISBN 978-1-909114-07-4

British Library Cataloguing in Publication Data
A catalogue record for this book is available from the British Library.

Publisher's Note:

Every care and attention has been put into the production of this book. If however, you find any errors they are our own, for which we seek Allāh's ﷻ forgiveness and the reader's pardon.

Published by:

JKN Publications
118 Manningham Lane
Bradford
West Yorkshire
BD8 7JF
United Kingdom

t: +44 (0) 1274 308 456 | w: www.jkn.org.uk | e: info@jkn.org.uk

Book Title: Stories for Children

Author: Shaykh Mufti Saiful Islām

Printed by Mega Printing in Turkey

"In the Name of Allāh, the Most Beneficent,
the Most Merciful"

Contents

Foreword

بِسْمِ اللّٰهِ الرَّحْمٰنِ الرَّحِيْمِ

"In the Name of Allāh, the Most Beneficent, the Most Merciful"

All praises be to Allāh ﷻ, the Lord of the worlds, the Creator of mankind and everything that is within the universe. Peace and salutations be upon His beloved Messenger Muhammad ﷺ.

May Allāh's ﷻ peace and blessings be upon you, my dear brothers, sisters and friends, wherever you may be. We praise Allāh ﷻ together and seek His forgiveness and refuge from the evils within ourselves and the mischief of our deeds. May Allāh ﷻ protect our souls. Āmīn!

I would like to take this opportunity to compliment a very special person, my beloved teacher, friend and spiritual guide, Shaykh Mufti Saiful Islām, for the sacrifices and humble efforts he has undertaken to propagate the dīn of Allāh ﷻ to Muslims and non-Muslims alike.

Stories for Children was first published in August 2003. Due to the overwhelming response from our readers world wide, it was only an inspiration for my beloved Shaykh to compile a more comprehensive and concise book for children, packed with wonderful and amazing stories. Remember, as much as children love reading these stories, I am certain that the adults would also!

It is only by the infinite grace and help from Allāh ﷻ that He has given my beloved Shaykh the ability to publish such books and I pray that he is able to publish more interesting and valuable books in the future. I would like to thank our sincere readers across the world for their contributions through all means.

Finally, I pray with tearful eyes and a weeping heart that Allāh ﷻ showers His mercy upon the Muslim ummah around the world who are suffering from the oppression of the oppressors and may He protect us from all the fitnah (trials) spreading in society. Āmīn!

Maulānā Muhammad Ibrāhīm Khān
Graduate of JKN
November 2014 / Muharram 1436

Introduction

All praises are due to Allāh ﷻ and may peace and blessings of Allāh ﷻ be upon the Final Prophet Muhammad ﷺ. It gives me great pleasure to present this book on the Stories for Children. The aim is to present to children true stories and incidents which contain moral lessons, in order to reform and correct their lives, according to the holy Qur'ān and ahādīth.

Today, children are reading books which are un-Islamic, immoral and detrimental to their upbringing and education. It is hoped that this book will serve as a stepping stone to inculcate in our children the love of Allāh ﷻ and His beloved Messenger ﷺ.

I would like to compliment my colleague Maulānā Muhammad Ibrāhīm Khān for helping me compile this book and all the brothers and sisters who assisted in whatever ways possible.

May Allāh ﷻ accept our humble efforts to further this cause and may these series of books prove to be useful for the purpose for which they have been written. Āmīn!

Shaykh Mufti Saiful Islām
November 2014 / Muharram 1436

The Holy Prophet's ﷺ Kindness

There was a woman who used to throw litter on the holy Prophet ﷺ whenever he used to go to the masjid for salāh. One day, as he was going past, he put his hand up to guard himself but no rubbish came down.

The holy Prophet ﷺ was surprised as to why the woman had not thrown rubbish that day, so he went to see the woman. He found that she was very ill. The holy Prophet ﷺ gave her some food which she ate. She felt better, looked at the holy Prophet ﷺ and said, "I know you. You are the same man that I used to throw my litter on."

The holy Prophet ﷺ replied, "I know but don't worry, I am still here to help you." This is how this woman became a Muslimah.

Moral:
Show kindness, even to those who treat you badly.

The Blind Snake

A gang of robbers were on their way to rob. They stopped at a place where there were three date trees. Two of the trees were green and had fruits. The third tree was dry.

One robber saw a bird flying with fruits from the green tree to the dry tree. This was done a few times. The robber became curious. He wanted to know what the bird was doing with the fruits so he climbed up the tree. He saw a snake at the top of the tree which was blind. Its mouth was open and the bird was putting dates into its mouth.

The robber was surprised and began to weep. He said, "O Lord! You have caused this bird to provide the snake with food and I am busy robbing others."

The robber broke his sword and begged Allāh ﷻ to forgive him. He told his friends everything. They all broke their swords and decided to give up their evil ways.

Moral:
Allāh ﷻ provides food for all living creatures!

Allāh ﷻ is with Us

The holy Prophet ﷺ left Makkah for Madīnah when he found out that the non-Muslims of Makkah were planning to kill him. Men were sent in all directions to look for him. A reward of one hundred camels was offered to anyone who captured the holy Prophet ﷺ.

The holy Prophet ﷺ and Sayyidunā Abū Bakr ؓ hid in a cave in Mount Thawr. One of the search parties reached the mouth of the cave. They were so close to the cave that those inside the cave could hear their voices. Sayyidunā Abū Bakr ؓ was concerned. He said, "O Messenger of Allāh! The enemy will see us." Rasūlullāh ﷺ was calm. He replied, "Don't be afraid! Surely, Allāh is with us."

A voice was then heard from outside saying, "Nobody has gone into the cave. Look at the spider's web over the mouth of the cave!" The search party left the cave and went away. The holy Prophet ﷺ and his friend, Sayyidunā Abū Bakr ؓ were protected by Allāh ﷻ.

Moral:
When you have trust in Allāh ﷻ, He will protect you.

Give up Islām or Give up Your Life

Sayyidunā Bilāl ☙ was the slave of Umayyah. Umayyah believed in many gods. When Sayyidunā Bilāl ☙ became a Muslim, Umayyah did not like it. He told Sayyidunā Bilāl ☙ to leave Islām and to pray to idols. Sayyidunā Bilāl ☙ would not. His master got angry.

Umayyah made him lie upon the burning sand in the hot sun. He put a heavy stone on his chest and said, "Give up Islām or die!" Sayyidunā Bilāl ☙ suffered much pain but he did not give up Islām. He would only say, "Ahad, Ahad! (Allāh ﷻ is) One! (Allāh ﷻ is) One!"

Umayyah and others took turns to whip him. He was left in the sun to die. They also dragged him in the streets. Again, the same words were said, "Ahad, Ahad! (Allāh ﷻ is) One! (Allāh ﷻ is) One!" Sayyidunā Bilāl ☙ never gave up Islām.

Moral:
We need to be strong upon Islām no matter what difficulties we face in our lives.

The Sahābah ﷺ Putting Others Before Themselves

Sayyidunā Abū Jahm ibn Hudhaifah ﷺ says, "In the battle of Yarmūk, I went out looking for my cousin who was in the thick of battle. I also took some water for him. I found him in the middle of the battle just about to die. I went forward to help with the little water I had. However, soon, another injured soldier beside him groaned and my cousin turned his face away and asked me to take the water to that person first.

I went towards this other person with the water. He turned out to be Sayyidunā Hishām ibn Abil Ās ﷺ. I had not reached him yet when he heard another groan of another person lying close by. Sayyidunā Hishām ﷺ pointed me in that direction but before I could reach the other person, he died. I quickly came back to Sayyidunā Hishām ﷺ and found him dead as well. Then, I hurried as fast as I could to my cousin, but unfortunately, in the meantime, he had also joined the other two."

<u>Moral:</u>
We should always try our best to think of other people's well-being and it is even more rewardable if we sacrifice our own needs for other people's needs.

Whatever Must Happen Will Happen

A group of friends were travelling when a heavy storm started, forcing them to take shelter in a cave. During the night, one of the friends, who was very hungry, decided to leave the cave to look for food. His friends told him to be careful as there were many wild beasts in the area. He left the cave and though he was very careful, a wild beast attacked and killed him.

In the morning, the friends left the cave feeling very sad that their dear friend had died. They walked on until they reached the home of a pious old man. They related their sad story to him and one of them said, "If he had not left the cave, he would have been here with us alive."

The pious man said, "No, if he had not left the cave, if Allāh ﷻ decided that he must die, he would have still died."

14

The friends understood and accepted that whatever had happened was by the will of Allāh ﷻ.

Moral:
Never dwell too much in 'ifs' and 'buts.' Rather, always be sure that whatever Allāh ﷻ wills, happens.

Putting the Holy Qur'ān Together

In the time of Sayyidunā Abū Bakr ﵁, the Muslim army went to fight the false prophet Musailamah. In the battle, there were many huffāz of the holy Qur'ān (people who know the Qur'ān by heart). However, at the end of the battle, though the Muslims won, a lot of the huffāz passed away.

Sayyidunā Umar ﵁ came to Sayyidunā Abū Bakr ﵁ and said that he was worried that if all the huffāz got martyred (killed), there would be no one left to keep the holy Qur'ān safe in their hearts. It would therefore be best if the holy Qur'ān was put together in a book form.

Sayyidunā Zaid ﷺ was given the job of collecting all the pieces of skins and tree barks, upon which the holy Qur'ān was written. Then, he put together the first copy of the holy Qur'ān in a book form.

Moral:
As Muslims, we must always try our best to protect the holy Qur'ān.

Bravery of a Small Boy

After migrating from Makkah to Madīnah, Rasūlullāh ﷺ sometimes sent his camels to eat grass in Ghābah, a small village five miles from Madīnah. Once, some armed bandits on horseback, led by Abdur Rahmān Fazāri, killed the innocent shepherd who looked after the camels and stole Rasūlullāh's ﷺ camels.

It just so happened that a young Sahābi named Salamah ibn Akwah ﷺ saw the whole event. Waiting for the right moment, he quickly ran up a hill and shouted for help in the direction of Madīnah.

Then, he began to chase the bandits on his own. As he got closer, he started firing arrows so quickly and accurately that the bandits thought they were being chased by a whole group of people.

Whenever a bandit turned around, Sayyidunā Salamah ﷺ hid behind a tree. He chased the bandits until he got Rasūlullāh's ﷺ camels back. The bandits also left behind thirty spears and many clothes.

A while later, a bandit named Uwainah ibn Hisn discovered that they were being chased by only one person. The bandits then surrounded Sayyidunā Salamah ﷺ from all sides, forcing him to scramble up a hill.

As the bandits came closer, Sayyidunā Salamah ﷺ shouted, "Stop and listen to what I have to say! Do you know who I am? I am the son of Akwah. By Allāh! If anyone of you were to chase me, he would never catch me. On the other hand, if I were to chase anyone of you, he would never be able to escape from me."

Thus, he kept them busy whilst he was hoping and waiting for help to arrive. As Sayyidunā Salamah ﷺ continued to keep them busy, a group of Muslim horsemen, led by Sayyidunā Akram Asadi ⚬, arrived. Sayyidunā Akram ⚬ attacked the leader of the bandits, Abdur-Rahmān Fazāri and knocked him off his horse. However, Abdur-Rahmān Fazāri killed Sayyidunā Akram ⚬ as he fell off his horse. Innā lillāhi wa innā ilaihi rāji'ūn (whenever a Muslim is faced with a difficulty he should recite this). Just then, more help arrived, forcing the bandits to retreat.

Young Sayyidunā Salamah ibn Akwah ⚬ begged Rasūlullāh ﷺ to allow him to go after the criminals but Rasūlullāh ﷺ did not give him permission. Historians have said that Sayyidunā Salamah ibn Akwah ⚬ was a professional archer and was faster than the fastest horse!
Subhān-Allāh!
His age? Only twelve!

Moral:
No matter what our age is, we should always be brave in supporting Allāh's ﷻ dīn and His Messenger ﷺ.

Allāh ﷻ Protects the Holy Qur'ān

A Jew once visited the famous caliph called Ma'mūn. The caliph invited the Jew to accept Islām but he refused and left the palace. A year later, the same Jew returned to the caliph's palace as a Muslim. The caliph was surprised and asked the Jew why he had finally become a Muslim.

The Jew said, "After leaving you, I wrote three copies of the Jewish holy Book and made many changes in them. I then sold those copies to the Jewish teachers and they sold out very quickly. I did the same to the Christian holy Book and the same thing happened. I then wrote three copies of the holy Qur'ān and made many changes in them. When I took them to the Muslim teachers, they did not accept the Qur'ān I had written because it had changes in it. Then, I realised that Allāh ﷻ does protect the holy Qur'ān and that Islām is the true religion."

Moral:
Allāh ﷻ has promised that He will preserve the holy Qur'ān and His promise is always true.

19

Allāh ﷻ Saves His Servants

A man was once fast asleep under a tree. Nearby, a huge snake was crawling and it came in the man's direction to attack him. Allāh ﷻ used a scorpion to help this man, although it was on the other side of the river.

Allāh ﷻ ordered a frog to come to the riverbank. The scorpion climbed onto the frog's back and the frog then swam across the river. When the frog hopped onto the opposite shore, the scorpion raced in the direction of the snake and the sleeping man. The snake was just about to bite the man when the scorpion stung the snake, causing it to die. The scorpion then left.

When the man woke up from his sleep, he wondered why a dead snake lay near him. Allāh ﷻ prevented the man from being harmed because he prayed to Allāh ﷻ regularly.

Moral:

When a person prays to Allāh ﷻ regularly, Allāh ﷻ helps him in ways he cannot imagine.

Kindness to Guests

Once a person came to the holy Prophet ﷺ. He did not feel well because he was hungry. He told the holy Prophet ﷺ, who then sent a Companion ؓ to bring something to eat from his home. The Companion ؓ came back with nothing as he could not find anything from the home of the holy Prophet ﷺ.

The holy Prophet ﷺ then asked his Companions ؓ, "Can anybody amongst you take this person as a guest for the night?" In response to this, an Ansāri Companion ؓ said, "O Prophet! I offer myself to become the host of this person."

He took the upset and hungry person to his home and said to his wife, "This man is the guest of the holy Prophet ﷺ. Treat him with full respect and leave no shortage in showing kindness to him. Do not hold back in offering the food you have at home."

The wife said, "By Allāh, the food I have set aside is sufficient for the children only. There is nothing else in the home."

The Companion of the holy Prophet ﷺ said to his wife, "Put the children to sleep. While they are asleep, we shall offer the food to the guest. At that moment, do not forget to put out the lamp and say you are setting the food. We shall accompany the guest and pretend to share the dinner with him so that he may eat to his fill."

The wife carried out the instructions of her husband. The children and the parents had to go without food for that night.

Moral:
True kindness and generosity is when a person sacrifices even his own things to please Allāh ﷻ and His holy Prophet ﷺ.

Allāh's ﷻ Help

When the disbelievers came to fight the Muslims at the Battle of Badr, there was a small number of Muslims and most of them did not have weapons. The disbelievers were greater in number and also had much more weapons.

The holy Prophet ﷺ made du'ā to Allāh ﷻ to help the Muslims against the enemies. Allāh ﷻ accepted the du'ā and sent down thousands of angels to fight on the side of the Muslims.

Many Muslims were surprised to see strangers on horseback with turbans on their heads, fighting on their side. They informed the holy Prophet ﷺ about this. He said to them, "These are angels that Allāh has sent to help you." The Muslims won this battle through Allāh's ﷻ help.

Moral:
When Muslims work for the sake of Allāh ﷻ, He will send down His help.

The Thirsty Dog

A man was going through a jungle when he became thirsty. He found a well and went down it to drink some water. When he came out, he saw a very thirsty dog licking the mud.

The man took pity on the dog, but he had nothing to bring the water out from the well with. So, he took off his leather socks and went down the well again. As he came up he held the socks filled with water with his mouth. He then gave the water to the dog to drink. Allāh ﷻ was very pleased with the man's act. He forgave him and entered him to Jannah.

Moral:
Even giving water to an animal is an act of sadaqah (charity). Never underestimate a good deed as it may be the one through which Allāh ﷻ grants you Jannah.

Cloth Maker

There was once a cloth maker who lived in a small house. He used to make clothes and sell them to the shopkeepers. Sometimes, the shopkeepers did not want to buy his clothes because they were of a very poor quality. So he decided to cheat the shopkeepers by showing them a good quality cloth but then giving them a poor quality one when they decided to buy it.

One day, the man dreamt that it was the Day of Judgement. Allāh ﷻ called him before the people and told him about the cheating. He was very embarrassed and afraid. The angels were then ordered to throw him into Hell. He woke up shivering from the scary dream. He asked for forgiveness at once and stopped his cheating.

Moral:
Once you find out you have done something bad, you should ask for forgiveness and stop doing it.

Enemies of the Holy Prophet ﷺ

The enemies of the holy Prophet ﷺ troubled him in every way. When he taught the Muslims about Islām, the enemies made fun of him.

Once, the holy Prophet ﷺ taught the Muslims that after death, Allāh ﷻ will bring them all back to life. An enemy came to the holy Prophet ﷺ with an old bone. He crushed it in front of him and teased him by saying, "O Muhammad, do you believe that this bone will come back to life?"

The holy Prophet ⬢ replied, "Yes, everything will be brought back to life." The enemy had a very bad death because he used to make fun of the holy Prophet ⬢ and Islām.

Moral:
No one should make fun of the holy Prophet ⬢ and Islām or else they may suffer a bad death.

Sayyidunā Umar ⬢ *Helps a Widow*

Once, Sayyidunā Umar ⬢ was patrolling the streets of Madīnah, when he spotted a tent just outside Madīnah. When he reached there, he saw a woman with children.

He noticed the children crying and there was a pot placed on the fire. He asked the woman why the children were crying. She replied that it was due to their hunger. Sayyidunā Umar ⬢ asked her what was in the pot. She told him that it was only water to make the children think that food was being prepared.

He hurried to Madīnah to the baitul-māl (Muslim treasury) to fetch flour, dates and other things to prepare a meal. He carried the food on his back and he himself prepared the meal and gave it to the woman to feed the children. The woman was very pleased with Sayyidunā Umar's ﷺ kindness and she made du'ā for him.

Moral:
We should always try our best to help those in need.

The Story of Alqamah ﷺ

Alqamah ﷺ was a very pious person. He spent his time in salāh and fasting. At the approach of death, he was unable to recite the kalimah in spite of the repeated talqīn (reminder) by those present. Alqamah's ﷺ wife sent a messenger to the holy Prophet ﷺ to inform him of Alqamah's ﷺ grave condition.

The holy Prophet ﷺ asked whether the parents of Alqamah ﷺ were alive. He was told that Alqamah's ﷺ mother was alive. The holy Prophet ﷺ asked the aged mother about

Alqamah ﷺ. She informed him that Alqamah was a very pious person; he passed his time in salāh and fasting. He also performed tahajjud, however he always disobeyed her for the sake of his wife. "I am therefore displeased with him," the mother said.

The holy Prophet ﷺ said, "It will be best for him if you forgave him." However, she refused. So, the holy Prophet ﷺ ordered Sayyidunā Bilāl ﷺ to gather fire wood and burn Alqamah ﷺ in the fire. On hearing this order, Alqamah's ﷺ mother asked in horror, "Will my child be burnt in the fire?"

The holy Prophet ﷺ said, "Yes! Compared to the punishment of Allāh ﷻ, our punishment is light. I take an oath by Allāh ﷻ that as long as you remain displeased with him, neither his salāh nor his sadaqah (charity) are accepted."Alqamah's ﷺ mother said, "I make you and all the people present witness that I have forgiven Alqamah."

The holy Prophet ﷺ addressing the gathering, said, "Go and see if the kalimah is on the tongue of Alqamah." After returning from Alqamah ﷺ, the people brought the good news that he was reciting the kalimah. Thus, he left this world with the kalimah on his lips.

After burying Alqamah ﷺ, the holy Prophet ﷺ said, "The curse of Allāh is on the one who causes difficulty to his mother. The curse of the angels and the curse of mankind are on him. Allāh neither accepts his compulsory nor his optional worship, as long as he does not repent and obey his mother. He has to gain her pleasure as best as he can. Allāh's pleasure depends on the mother's pleasure and His displeasure depends on her displeasure."

Moral:
We must always strive to please our parents because if we don't, then our good deeds will not be accepted by Allāh ﷻ.

100 Murders

A man from a nation of the past murdered ninety-nine people. He then asked who the most learned person was. He was told to go and see a certain Christian monk. So he went to him and asked, "I've killed ninety-nine people. Is there any chance of forgiveness for me?"

The monk answered, "What? You've killed ninety-nine people and you expect forgiveness? No chance!"

So the man killed the monk and completed one hundred murders. The killer asked again as to who was the most learned person. He was directed to a scholar. He went to him and asked, "I've killed a hundred people. Is there any hope of forgiveness for me?"

The scholar replied, "Yes, nothing can stand between you and repentance. Go to this far land; in it are righteous people who serve Allāh ﷻ. Join them in the service of Allāh ﷻ and never return to your home town because it is an evil place."

So the man started travelling to that place. However, on the way he died. He had only covered half the distance.

A dispute arose between the angels of Jahannam and the angels of Jannah as to who should take charge of the soul. The angels of Jannah argued that he was on his way to repent and to do a good deed, while the angels of Jahannam pleaded that he had never done a good deed in his life.

Then, Allāh ﷻ sent another angel to tell them that he shall be the judge between them. The angel told them to measure the distance between the two lands, the land of evil and the land of good which he was heading to. He would belong to the land he was nearer to. So he would be punished if he was nearer to the land of evil and be rewarded if he was nearer to the land of good.

In the meantime, Allāh ﷻ sent more angels to quickly shorten the land between him and the land of good so that Allāh ﷻ could reward him as he made the intention of doing good deeds and repenting.

The angels carried out the measurement and found the land of good people to be closer. The angels of mercy took charge of him and took him towards Jannah.

Moral:
We should never give up on Allāh's ﷻ mercy or believe He would not forgive us no matter how bad our mistakes are. Allāh ﷻ loves those who repent.

Obedience To Ones Parents

Sayyidunā Mūsā عليه السلام was one of Allāh's ﷻ greatest Prophets who lived long before us. Once, Sayyidunā Mūsā عليه السلام asked Allāh ﷻ who would be his companion in Jannah. Allāh ﷻ told him to go to a certain place. He went to this place and discovered a man who was selling meat. Sayyidunā Mūsā عليه السلام stayed with him for the day and he offered to host Sayyidunā Mūsā عليه السلام during the night.

When they reached home, the first thing this man did was to prepare the meat which he had bought for their meal. He then helped his mother by washing her and then feeding her. Due to this, she prayed, "May you be the companion of the Prophet Mūsā عليه السلام in Jannah." This prayer from his mother was because of his obedience to her.

<u>Moral:</u>
Our parents' du'ās are readily accepted so we should always aim to please them so that they could make good du'ās for us.

Speak the Truth

Once, there lived a pious man named Abdul Qādir Jīlāni ﷺ. When he was a young boy, he studied in his town. After some time, he decided to travel to another town to further his Islamic studies.

When he left home, his mother gave him forty gold coins which she had sewn on the inside of his kurta (shirt). As he was leaving, she advised him never to lie in any situation.

Whilst on the journey, Abdul Qādir Jīlāni's ﷺ caravan was attacked by thieves. They stole all they could find with the people within the caravan. When they asked Abdul Qādir ﷺ if he had any money, he replied, "Yes."

When they searched him, they could not find the money so they told the gang-leader. When Abdul Qādir ﷺ told them where it was, they were so surprised that he had told the truth. They asked Abdul Qādir ﷺ why he had been so honest. He explained what his mother advised him when he left home.

The gang-leader then said to himself, "If Abdul Qādir could listen and obey the advice of his mother, then how is it not possible for us to follow the commands of Allāh ﷻ?" After this, all the thieves repented and became better Muslims.

The reason for them doing so was only because Abdul Qādir ﷺ did not lie about the money which he had with him because his mother told him never to lie.

Moral:
We should always listen to what our parents tell us to do as well as be honest and truthful. We never know who could like our good behaviour and want to do good because of us.

Who Will Save You?

Once the holy Prophet ﷺ and his friends were returning from a journey. They decided to rest for a while. The holy Prophet ﷺ hung his sword on a tree and lay down to sleep. An enemy saw the holy Prophet ﷺ sleeping and decided to attack him.

He grabbed the sword and standing over the holy Prophet ﷺ, he asked, "Tell me, who can save you from me?" The holy Prophet ﷺ calmly replied, "Allāh." The enemy got such a fright by this answer that he dropped the sword. The holy Prophet ﷺ picked up the sword and asked him, "Now, tell me, who can save you?" The man replied, "None besides you." The holy Prophet ﷺ forgave the man and let him go.

Moral:
When we have 100% trust in Allāh ﷻ, He will save us from any difficulty.

Kindness to the Mother

It was a late night. Bāyazīd was a young boy. His mother was sleeping while he was learning his lessons. Suddenly, the mother said in a sleepy voice, "A cup of water my son; I am thirsty."

Bāyazīd immediately went to fetch the water, but he found the pot empty. He went out of the house to the spring. By the time he returned, his mother had fallen back into deep sleep.

What was the young boy Bāyazīd to do? If he awakened his

mother, it would be giving her trouble. He decided to sit silently next to his mother with the cup of water in his hand.

At last, the mother opened her eyes and found Bāyazīd was sitting by her side. The mother remembered what she had said to her son in the early part of the night.

She was very pleased with her son and hugged him. She prayed to Allāh ﷻ to be pleased with him. The mother's prayer was answered. In later life, the boy became a pious saint!

Moral:
Always be good to your parents because through their du'ās we could reach great success.

Key to Paradise

One day, the holy Prophet ﷺ was sitting amongst his Companions when he asked, "Who amongst you began the day by fasting?" All were silent except Sayyidunā Abū Bakr ﷺ who replied, "I did."

The holy Prophet ﷺ then asked, "Who amongst you fed the poor today?" Again, it was Sayyidunā Abū Bakr ؓ who replied, "I did."

The holy Prophet ﷺ then asked, "Who amongst you visited the sick today?" It was Sayyidunā Abū Bakr ؓ once more who answered, "I did."

The holy Prophet ﷺ then said, "If these virtues come together in a person, it will be the key to Paradise for him."

Moral:
Fasting, feeding the poor and visiting the sick are all good deeds which take a person towards Jannah (Paradise).

A Doctor's Complaint

A doctor came from Syria to Madīnah. With the permission of the holy Prophet ﷺ, he opened his surgery in the city of Madīnah. The doctor offered to treat the poor free of charge.

He stayed in Madīnah for some time, but the Muslims hardly went to him for treatment. He was surprised and puzzled. As he was a foreigner and a Christian, he felt that perhaps the people did not trust him.

He put his complaint to the holy Prophet 🕌. The holy Prophet 🕌 assured him that what he thought was wrong. The Muslims of Madīnah were in good health, thus there was no need to go to a doctor.

"How is that possible?" The doctor asked. The holy Prophet 🕌 replied, "Muslims are not allowed to eat unclean and harmful foods. They are required to eat good, nutritious and healthy foods. They only eat when they are really hungry. When they are hungry, they do not eat too much but they stop eating before their hunger is fully satisfied."

The doctor agreed that these were simple rules for staying healthy. There was no need for him in such a place. He therefore left Madīnah to go elsewhere.

Moral:
Like the Muslims of Madīnah, we should always eat healthily to protect our health and save us from illnesses.

Be Kind to All

Once a man asked permission to meet the holy Prophet ﷺ. Permission was given. "Let him come in," said the holy Prophet ﷺ, "He is known as the worst member of his tribe."

When the man came in, the holy Prophet ﷺ greeted him politely. He spoke to him very gently and kindly. This surprised Sayyidah Ā'ishah ﵂.

As soon as the man was gone, she asked the holy Prophet ﷺ why he had spoken to him so kindly if he was not a good man. The holy Prophet ﷺ replied, "The worst man in the eyes of Allāh ﷻ is he who stops meeting a person because of the person's bad habits."

Moral:
Even if somebody is a bad person, we should always remain polite and well-mannered with him.

A Trial

There were three men who lived a long time ago. One was bald, one had a skin disease and one was blind. Allāh ﷻ wished to test them so he sent an angel to them. First, the angel went to the one with the skin disease and asked him, "What things do you love the most?"

"Light colour and fine skin," he answered "I want to get rid of this disease for which everyone treats me badly," he added. The angel touched him and with the grace of Allāh ﷻ, he was cured. He was now a handsome man with light and healthy skin.

"What kind of animals do you like the most?" the angel asked. He replied, "Camels." The angel gave him some camels and prayed, "May Allāh ﷻ bless you with the benefits of these camels."

Then, the angel went to the bald man and put the same question to him, "What things do you love the most?"

"I would love a thick growth of hair on my head so that I may get rid of my baldness for which everybody makes fun of me," said the bald man. The angel touched him and in a short time, the baldness vanished. Allāh ﷻ blessed him with beautiful hair.

The angel now asked him the next question, "What kind of animals do you like the most?" He replied, "Cows." The angel gave him some cows and prayed, "May Allāh ﷻ bless you with the benefits of these cows."

The angel then went to the blind man and repeated the same question, "What would you love the most?" "I wish Allāh ﷻ would restore my eye sight, so that I might see the people," said the blind mind. The angel touched him too. No sooner had the angel touched him, that Allāh ﷻ restored his eyesight.

The angel now put the next question to him, "What kind of animal do you like the most?" "I would love to have some goats." The angel gave him some goats.

After some time, the animals of the three men gave birth to young ones. By the grace of Allāh ﷻ, the animals brought good fortune to them. The three men, who once had been a man with skin disease, a bald man and a blind man, now had a good number of camels, cows and goats each.

After a long time, the same angel, this time disguised as someone with bad skin, came to the man who once had bad skin and said, "I am a poor man. I have spent all of my money during my journey. I have lost all of my hope. It is only Allāh ﷻ that I can depend on. I am on the lookout for some help. In the name of Allāh ﷻ, Who has blessed you with a charming personality, beautiful appearance and fair skin and has also blessed you with wealth in the form of camels, I seek your financial support, Sir. Can you help me?" The man said harshly, "Sorry, I can't help you as I have got many other things to deal with."

The angel revealed the facts about his past life. He said, "I recognise you well. You once had bad skin and people used to dislike you. You were needy and helpless. Then Allāh ﷻ favoured you with health and wealth."

"I have inherited this property from my forefathers and I am the sole heir to this fortune," the man said in pride. At this, the angel said, "May Allāh ﷻ put you in the same position you were in before, if you are a liar."

Then, the angel disguised as a bald man, went to the man who once had been bald and asked for help. The man also refused to help him. The angel said, "May Allāh ﷻ turn you into what you were before, if you are a liar."

Finally, the angel disguised as a blind man, appeared before the man who had once been blind. The angel related his story in these words, "I am a poor traveller. I have spent all my money during my journey. Now, I have nothing except my faith in Allāh ﷻ to depend on. In this condition, I have no choice but to seek your help. In the name of Allāh ﷻ, Who has blessed you with eyesight, I beg from you a goat to bring ease to my journey."

Hearing this story, the man replied in the following words, "I was indeed a blind man some time ago. Allāh ﷻ restored my eyesight. I was needy, he turned me into a wealthy man. I offer you whatsoever I possess. You may take whatever you like and leave whatever you dislike. By Allāh ﷻ, I shall not refuse to give you anything you ask for in the name of Allāh ﷻ."

The angel then told him the good news, "You may keep your belongings with you. You three men were put on a trial and you are the one who succeeded. Allāh ﷻ is pleased with you, while the other two will see His anger."

Moral:
No matter how much we have in this life, we must always remember it is from Allāh 🌺 and be grateful to Him.

Truth Spoken By Shaytān

The following story has been narrated by Sayyidunā Abū Hurairah ⚘. Once, the holy Prophet 🌸 gave me the duty of looking after the grains, which were collected because of the charity given by the people, on the occasion of Īdul Fitr. At night, a man came into the store and filled a bag with grains to take away. I caught him on the spot and said to him, "I shall take you to the holy Prophet 🌸." The thief said, "I am a poor and needy man and have a large family to support. My need led me to do this." Hearing this, I set him free.

The next morning, when I went to the holy Prophet 🌸, he said, "Abū Hurairah, how did you treat your prisoner last night?" I said, "He told me his need and spoke of looking after a large family. Thereupon I took pity on him and released him." The holy Prophet 🌸 said, "He told a lie and he will come again."

I was sure that the thief would come again as the holy Prophet ﷺ had told me. I stayed on the lookout for him. He did come and began to collect the grains. I caught him and said, "I shall take you to the holy Prophet ﷺ."

He again begged me for mercy. He said, "I am needy and it is necessary for me to look after my family." I again took pity on the thief and let him go.

The next morning, when I paid a visit to the holy Prophet ﷺ, he said, "Abū Hurairah, what did the prisoner say last night?"

"He described his difficulty and desperate need in such a manner that I could not help but take pity on him, so I released him," I replied. The holy Prophet ﷺ said, "He told a lie to you. He will soon come again."

I again expected him and he did not fail to come the third time. As he was going to leave with the bag full of grains, I caught him by his hand and said, "Now, I will definitely take you to the holy Prophet ﷺ."

He said, "If you release me, I shall teach you words which if you read them, they will cause you to be blessed with the favours of Allāh 錢."

"What are those words?" I asked. He said, "Recite Āyatul Kursi when you go to bed before sleeping. Allāh 錢 will protect you all night and Shaytān will not come close to you until the morning." Having learnt these words, I set him free.

The next morning, I went to the holy Prophet 錢 as usual. He asked me, "What did the prisoner say to you last evening?"

"He guaranteed me that if I release him, he would teach me words which would help me to win Allāh's 錢 favours. At this, I released him."

"What are these words?" asked the holy Prophet 錢. I then told him the thief's words which were, recite Āyatul-Kursi when you go to bed before sleeping; Allāh 錢 will protect you all night and Shaytān will not come near you till morning.

At this, the holy Prophet 錢 said the following words, "No

doubt he is a great liar but this time, he has spoken the truth. Do you know, Abū Hurairah, whom you have been talking with for the last three nights?" "I don't know," I said. "He is Shaytān," replied the holy Prophet ﷺ.

Moral:

Āyatul-Kursi should be read every night before sleeping for protection. Even Shaytān testifies to this.

Treat your Neighbours Kindly

The Companions of the holy Prophet ﷺ were called Sahābah ﷺ.

There was a Sahābi by the name of Abdullāh ﷺ. He was very pious and obedient to Allāh ﷻ and His Messenger ﷺ.

Once, a sheep was slaughtered at the home of Sayyidunā Abdullāh ﷺ. From his neighbours there was a Jewish family.

It so happened that Sayyidunā Abdullāh ﷺ went somewhere. When he returned home in the evening, he asked his family, "Did you send some meat to the neighbours?"

They said, "But they are Jews. Why should meat be sent there?"

Sayyidunā Abdullāh ◈ then said, "So what if they are Jews? They are our neighbours after all."

The holy Prophet ◉ reminded us many times to treat our neighbours kindly, whether they are Muslims or non-Muslims.

Thereafter, Sayyidunā Abdullāh ◈ did not eat the meat until some of it was sent to the neighbours.

Moral:
Always be kind to your neighbours even if they are non-Muslims.

Hide Your Secrets

Sayyidunā Anas ◈ was a great Sahābi. From his childhood, he was very pious.

Once he was playing with other children. The holy Prophet ﷺ passed by and greeted the children. Then, he called Sayyidunā Anas ؓ and sent him for some work. It took Sayyidunā Anas ؓ some time to complete the work.

When he came home, his mother asked, "Where did you go for so long Anas?" Sayyidunā Anas ؓ replied, "The holy Prophet ﷺ sent me for some work." His mother asked, "What work was it?" He said, "That is a secret."

So his mother said, "Listen, O my son, don't ever tell this secret of the holy Prophet ﷺ to anyone." Sayyidunā Anas ؓ always remembered this and did not tell it to anyone during his lifetime.

Thābit was a close student of Sayyidunā Anas ؓ. One day, he told Thābit about this incident and said, "Thābit, had I told anyone this secret it would have been you."

Moral:
It is very important that we keep other people's secrets and do not share them with anybody.

The Mysterious Helper

In the city of Madīnah, there lived a poor, blind woman. She had no one to take care of her.

Sayyidunā Umar ◈ used to bring water for her, sweep her floor and milk her goat. During the time when Sayyidunā Abū Bakr ◈ was the khalīfah (caliph), there was a change.

Sayyidunā Umar ◈ would find that when he arrived at the house of the blind woman, the work he used to do, was already done!

One day, he decided to go earlier than usual, hide himself and watch who this mysterious helper was. It was none other than the khalīfah himself! Sayyidunā Abū Bakr ◈ believed that the khalīfah was not the ruler of the Muslims but rather, he was their servant.

Moral:
When we become leaders we should still help others.

Words and Action Should be the Same

There was once a boy who loved eating sweets. He always asked for sweets from his father. His father was a poor man who could not always afford sweets for his son. However, the little boy did not understand this and demanded sweets all the time. The boy's father thought hard about how to stop the child asking for so many sweets.

There was a pious man living nearby at that time. The boy's father had an idea. He decided to take the boy to the great man who might be able to persuade the child to stop asking for sweets all the time.

The boy and his father went to this great man. The father asked him, "O great saint, could you ask my son to stop asking for sweets which I cannot afford?"

The great man was in difficulty because he liked sweets himself. How could he ask the boy to give up asking for sweets?

The pious man told the father to bring his son back after

one month. During that month, the pious man gave up eating sweets. When the boy and his father returned after a month, the pious man said to the boy, "My dear child, please stop asking for sweets which your father cannot afford to give to you!"

From then on, the boy stopped asking for sweets. The boy's father asked the pious man, "Why did you not ask my son to give up asking for sweets when we came to you a month ago?"

The pious man replied, "How could I ask your child to give up eating sweets when I loved sweets myself. In the last month, I gave up eating sweets myself."

Moral:
A person's example is much more powerful than just his words. When we ask someone to do something, we must do it ourselves also. We cannot expect others to do what we do not do ourselves.

Two Young Pigeons

The holy Prophet ﷺ was sitting and talking to his Companions ﷺ.

A man came up to them and said, "A wonderful thing happened. I was passing by a bush and heard a chirping noise. I peeped in and saw two young pigeons. I picked them up in my wrapper and walked on. By this time, the mother came and saw the empty nest. She began flying above us. I opened my wrapper and how strange! The mother pigeon came down into my wrapper and sat over the young ones. Look! They are still in my wrapper."

The holy Prophet ﷺ saw the birds and said to the man, "Go at once and put them back in their nest. A mother has so much love. How full of worry is the heart of this mother pigeon for her young ones."

After seeing this example of a mother caring for her children, the holy Prophet ﷺ turned to his Companions ﷺ and said, "Allāh has far more love and concern for His creation."

Moral:
A mother's love is very strong but Allāh's ﷻ love for us is even stronger.

Taqdīr - Fate

Once a child swallowed a stone and became very ill. The parents did not know what the cause of the illness was. They gave the child different types of medicines and visited various doctors.

Finally, one doctor discovered the problem and decided to operate on the child to remove the stone. After the stone was removed, the child felt much better but after two days, the child passed away.

The parents were very shocked and asked, "Why did our child pass away even after the stone was removed?"

They were informed by learned people that according to the child's taqdīr, he would only live in this world for a certain number of years and nothing can change this.

<u>Moral:</u>

Everybody's death is already written by Allāh ﷻ so we can never fix or estimate a time for it.

Following the Prophet ﷺ

Sayyidunā Īsā ﷺ was once walking with his disciples when they reached a river bank. Obviously, the disciples stopped walking, but to their astonishment, Sayyidunā Īsā ﷺ continued walking until he was miraculously walking on water.

The disciples stared in amazement and shock at their beloved Prophet. Sayyidunā Īsā ﷺ saw that his disciples were not following him so he asked them the reason.

The disciples replied, "O Īsā, our beloved Prophet, it is clear that if we try to walk on the water, we will drown."

"You will not drown unless you take your gazes away from my feet. So keep looking at my feet or you will indeed drown and I will not be able to save you from Allāh,"

Sayyidunā Īsā ﷺ replied.

So, the disciples stepped into the water, careful not to take their eyes off their beloved Prophet's feet, but Shaytān, as he is the enemy of mankind, planted a thought in one of the disciples' mind to look at how he is walking on the water.

The disciple, remembering the instructions of Sayyidunā Īsā ﷺ, continued looking at his beloved Prophet's feet. Shaytān tempted him again and again. Shaytān instructed him that if he had a glimpse of his own feet for a second and then looked back towards Sayyidunā Īsā's ﷺ feet, surely there would be no harm. As soon as he did this, he started to drown. He cried out for help to Sayyidunā Īsā ﷺ but to no avail.

Moral:
Take a lesson from this story. The disciple drowned due to the fact that he disobeyed the command of his Prophet. Likewise, if we do not succeed in maintaining a firm hold on the holy Qur'ān and the Sunnah, which the holy Prophet ﷺ advised us to follow, then surely, we would drown in a sea of sins.

Sayyidunā Umar's ﷺ *Hijrah (Migration) to Madīnah*

Sayyidunā Umar ﷺ is well known for his bravery and great courage by all. When the Muslims were very weak in the beginning, the holy Prophet ﷺ prayed to Allāh ﷺ to strengthen the Muslims with Sayyidunā Umar's ﷺ Islām. This prayer was answered by Allāh ﷺ in no time.

Sayyidunā Abdullāh ibn Mas'ūd ﷺ says, "We could not pray our salāh openly in Makkah until Sayyidunā Umar ﷺ had accepted Islām."

Sayyidunā Ali ﷺ says, "Early migrants to Madīnah left Makkah quietly and secretly, due to the fear of the Quraysh, but when Sayyidunā Umar ﷺ decided to migrate, he hung his sword from his neck, held his bow in his hand and took a large number of arrows with him. He first went to Makkah, performed tawāf most confidently, prayed his salāh most calmly and then went to the different groups of Quraysh, declaring before each of them, "Whosoever does not mind his mother crying upon him, his wife becoming a widow and his children becoming orphans, may come out of Makkah and face me." No one dared to face him.

<u>Moral:</u>
Like Sayyidunā Umar ﷺ, we should also be proud of our dīn even if others around us are not following the right path.

Allāh ﷻ *Knows Best*

Once, a king and his minister set out on a journey to hunt animals. It was the habit of the minister to say, "Whatever happened is good," every time anything happened, meaning, Allāh ﷻ has done good.

When they arrived at the forest, the king took out his bow and arrow. The arrow pricked his hand and it started to bleed. The minister on seeing this said, "Whatever happened is good."

The king became extremely angry and ordered the minister to be taken to jail saying, "I have started to bleed and you say it is good!"

So, the minister was sent to jail. On his way he said, "Whatever happened is good." The king looked at him in confusion, then carried on hunting until he felt tired. He laid down under a tree to rest and fell asleep.

The king was unaware that man-eating tigers (who eat humans alive) roamed around in that area. One of these tigers saw the king and came to eat him. The king woke up but it was too late for him to protect himself. He was helpless and death appeared in front of him. However, the tigers only ate uninjured and pure prey. To the king's surprise, because the king's hand was bleeding, the tiger sniffed him, left him and went away.

The king remembered the minister's words when his hand had started bleeding, "Whatever happened is good."

The king then returned to his palace, called his minister and told him the whole story. Then he said to the minister, "I understand that by me getting pricked on the hand, I got saved from being eaten alive, but when I sent you to jail, you said, 'Whatever happened is good.' I did not see any good in that."

The minister said, "You were saved from being eaten alive by the tiger because of the cut from your arrow, but I did not have any injuries, so if I had not been sent to jail, the tiger would have eaten me alive!"

Moral:
Allāh ﷻ plans everything for a reason. Sometimes when a bad thing happens to us, it leads to something good, so we should be patient during hardships and trust that Allāh ﷻ will give us something good from it.

The Fruits of Patience

A camel and a jackal were good friends. They ate together, drank together and lived together.

One day, they decided to eat the melons that grew in a field on the other side of the river. However, the jackal was a little worried, "You're so tall; you'll paddle through the river. How will I manage?" he asked.

"Don't you worry," said the camel, "I'll carry you on my back of course."

So they reached the field and started eating to their heart's content. The jackal, being much smaller, was soon full while the camel had just begun. The jackal, as was his custom, sat at the edge of the field and started howling loudly to digest his food.

"O friend!" the camel begged, "Don't howl so loud, lest the farmer hears you and comes and then beats us."

"Sorry, but if I don't howl after dinner, I get cramps in my tummy," said the jackal stubbornly.

As was expected, the farmer heard the jackal and came running with a big stick in his hand. As soon as he saw him, the jackal ran and hid in the bushes but the camel, being so large, could not hide. The poor animal was given a good beating. At last, he managed to escape and reached the riverbank. He found the jackal waiting there for him.

"Let's go home," the camel said quietly. So, the jackal hauled himself onto the camel's back and then stepped into the river. They had reached the middle of the river, when the camel began to sit down.

"What are you doing? For God's sake, don't sit here or I'll drown!" cried the alarmed jackal.

"My dear friend! If I don't bathe after dinner, I get cramps in my tummy," replied the camel calmly. Saying so, he bent his legs. The jackal slid, fell into the water and was carried far away by the current.

Moral:
We should always be good to others because if we are not, the same difficulty may befall us and we will regret treating them badly.

The Ant and the Pigeon

A long time ago, there lived a pigeon on a tree next to a small stream. He had no friends, so he often felt very lonely. At such times, he would wish for a friend to talk and play with.

One day, the pigeon was sitting on a branch of the tree and looking around. Just then, he saw a small ant near the bank of the stream. Perhaps, the ant was trying to drink water. Suddenly, the wind blew the ant into the stream.

Now the pigeon began to watch the ant very closely. He saw that she was struggling very hard to swim towards the bank but each time she moved a little towards the bank, the water would push her back again. This happened many times, yet the ant did not give up.

After some time, the pigeon sensed that the ant was exhausted due to her long struggle. The pigeon now began to think of some way to help the ant. He looked around himself. Suddenly, he had an idea. He plucked a leaf from the tree and flew to her in the stream. He quickly put the leaf next to her and she gratefully jumped onto it.

In a short time, she reached the bank on the floating leaf. Thanking the pigeon for his timely help, the ant promised to repay his debt sometime in the future.

Then she added, "I live in a hole near this tree. Today you have helped me and I would like to be friends with you. Would you be my friend?"

The pigeon had always wanted a friend. So he agreed to be the ant's friend.

Now, the two friends would sit together and talk for hours. They would tell each other about the new places they had visited. They would share each and every joy as well as their sorrows. They would even keep a watch over each other's houses when the other was not around. Thus, their days were passing happily and peacefully.

One day, the ant was resting in the sun. The pigeon had gone on his daily trip to get his food. Just then, the ant saw a hunter. He was standing some distance from the pigeon's nest and gazing at it intently. The ant quickly sensed the danger. She decided to inform her friend about the hunter and advise him to be careful.

After some time, the ant saw the pigeon flying back. She got up to talk to him. As she did so, she saw the hunter standing behind a rock. He was taking aim to shoot an arrow at the pigeon. Realising that there was no time to warn him, she decided to act.

The ant immediately began to run fast towards the hunter. She reached him just as he was about to shoot the arrow.

She quickly got onto his foot and stung him. The hunter jumped high in the air due to the pain and his arrow missed its aim. The pigeon saw the arrow passing by him and he quickly flew away.

In this way, the ant kept her promise and saved the pigeon's life.

Moral:
When we are good to others, they will be good to us in return.

The Virtues of Bismillāh

Bishr Hāfi ﷺ was among the great saints. However, in the beginning of his life, he used to get drunk with wine.

Once, he found a piece of paper on the road on which 'Bismillāh' was written. He picked it up with love, placed it on his eyes, applied perfume to it and put it away with respect. Then, he drank some wine and slept the night away. Meanwhile, Hasan Basri ﷺ (also a great saint) was told in a dream that he should give good news to Bishr Hāfi ﷺ and take him out from the pub.

Hasan Basri ﷺ immediately went to the pub. The people looked at him in shock and asked him what the matter was.

"Why have you come to the pub?" one asked. He replied, "Don't get me wrong. I have not come here by my own will. Allāh has sent me to fetch Bishr Hāfi. Therefore, tell me where he is."

The people pointed towards Bishr Hāfi ﷺ who was lying down in a drunken state. Hasan Basri ﷺ went to him and managed to make him conscious. He then took him away.

When he had completely recovered, he gave him the glad tidings of Allāh ﷺ to him. A sound from the unseen was heard, "O Bishr, you respected My Name, therefore, I have increased your honour. You purified My Name and applied perfume to it, hence, I have purified you of sins as a result and applied My perfume on you."

In this manner, in a short while, he changed from an alcoholic to a perfect friend of Allāh ﷺ.

Moral:
Glory be to Allāh ﷻ! What great mercy He has. Like Bishr Hāfi ؓ, we should also respect the holy Qur'ān and everything connected to it so that we can be classed with the friends of Allāh ﷻ.

Ambar - The Fish

The holy Prophet ﷺ sent towards the seashore an army of three hundred men, under the leadership of Sayyidunā Abū Ubaidah ؓ in the 8th year of hijri. He gave them a bag full of dates for their food.

They had hardly been out for fifteen days when they ran short of food. In order to provide the group with food, Sayyidunā Qais ؓ began buying three camels daily from his own men to feed the army, with a promise to pay them on return to Madīnah.

The leader, seeing that the slaughter of camels would deprive the army of their only means of travel, stopped him. He collected the dates that had been left with each person and stored them in a bag. He would give one date to each man as his daily food.

When Sayyidunā Jābir ﷺ later on mentioned this story to his students, one of his students asked, "How did you manage to live upon one date for the whole day?"

He replied, "We longed even for that one date, when the whole stock was finished. When we were on the verge of starvation, we dipped the dry tree leaves in water and ate them."

When they reached this stage of hunger, Allāh ﷻ had mercy on them, for He always brings ease after every difficulty.

A big fish known as Ambar was thrown out of the sea for them. The fish was so big that they lived off it for eighteen days. They also filled their bags with the remaining portion, which lasted them right up to Madīnah.

When the story was mentioned to the holy Prophet ﷺ, he said, "The fish was a rizq (food) arranged for you by Allāh ﷻ."

Moral:

Allāh ﷻ always gives us ease after hardship. Therefore we should remain patient during hardships like the Companions of the holy Prophet ﷺ did and hope for reward.

The Saint and the Atheist

One day, a great saint was walking on the bank of a river when an atheist approached him and asked, "O wise man, I want to see God with my own eyes. Can you arrange that for me?"

The saint answered, "God cannot be seen with the external eyes. He can only be realised."

The atheist replied, "Whatever you may say, I will never believe that God cannot be seen or touched."

The saint thought for a moment and instructed his companions, "Throw this man into the river."

The companions acted accordingly. While struggling for his

life, the man cried out, "Save me, wise man! I beg you, save me!" The companions pulled him out as the atheist gasped for air.

The saint then strictly ordered his companions, "Tie his hands together, throw him into the river and never save him again."

The companions complied and the man was thrown into the river with his hands tied together.

The atheist cried out, "Save me, Merciful Lord, there is none else but You Who can save me!"

The atheist was pulled out by the saint's order. The man started trembling. The saint went to the atheist and said, "You were shouting, 'Merciful Lord'. Did you see God?"

The man answered, "Yes, when all hopes vanished, I took His shelter. Then the door of my mind opened out and I saw Him there."

Moral:
Just because we cannot see Allāh 🕮 does not mean He

does not exist. When nobody else can help us, we will always turn to Him.

Burden and Patience

Once upon a time, there were two friends, one of whom was patient by nature while the other was impatient.

One day, when they were carrying baskets full of fruits on their heads from their village to a nearby town to sell, the impatient man soon started to complain.

"Hey, I'm tired. I can't go on. I can't stand this any more!"

"Are you serious? We've just started!" exclaimed the patient man. "I don't care. I can't go on," replied the impatient man. "I wonder why you're like this?" the patient man asked.

"I know your load is heavier than mine and you're not stronger than me either, but I don't understand how you can laugh and be happy while you're carrying it!" was the impatient man's response.

"You know, I've put a kind of plant on my load which lightens it and makes it quite easy for me to bear," said the patient man. "Really? Is that right? Can you give me a piece of that plant?"

"Certainly. It is the plant of patience which lightens any load."

Moral:
If we are patient during challenges, it will ease the hardship of the task for us. In contrast, if we become frustrated and negative, it will only make things harder.

The Tongue

Once, the great Emperor of Yemen said to his servant, "Go to the market and purchase the best part of a sheep."

The servant rushed to the market and asked the butcher to weigh one pound of sheep's tongue.

Having paid the butcher, he returned to the palace, entered

the Emperor's chamber and said, "Here it is your highness; the best part of a sheep."

Emperor: "What is it?"
Servant: "The sheep's tongue, O emperor."
Emperor: "Is that the best part of a sheep?"
Servant: "Of course, your highness."

Early next morning, the emperor sent the servant to the market again with some coins and asked him to buy the worst part of a sheep.

Likewise, the servant proceeded to the market, paid the butcher for one pound of tongue and presented it to the emperor.

Emperor: "Are you certain this is the worst part of the sheep?"
Servant: "Yes, great emperor."
Emperor: "Why have you considered the tongue as being the best part as well as the worst part?"

Servant: "Your majesty, the tongue is peace, the tongue is wisdom and the tongue is love. So, this is why the tongue is the best part. However, the tongue is also destruction, stupidity and hatred and this is why I consider it as the worse part. By the proper use of the tongue, you may become pious but by the same tongue used improperly, you may become wicked."

Delighted by his wisdom, the emperor handed him a bag of golden coins.

Moral:
We must always use our tongues wisely because they can either be a source of doing good or a source of doing bad.

Nobody Cares for Me

A man was on his death bed. His family understood that he was passing away. So, his family members and relatives began to weep sitting around him.

Suddenly, the sick man spoke out, "All of you be quiet!" He then went to question his family members,

"O my dear father, why are you crying?"
"My son! I am crying because I'll break down and be lonely if you leave," replied his grieving father.

"Mother dear! Why are you crying?" asked the ill man. "O my dear son, I always hoped that you would assist me in my old age, but you are leaving before me," replied the mother.

"What makes you cry, my dear wife?"
"My children are going to be orphaned. I shall have to look after them all alone, without your warm companionship. I can't stop the tears."

"And why are you weeping, my dear children?"
"Who will take care of us and provide our livelihood after you are gone?" answered one of the children.

"Alas! What a pity! I have given my whole life to you all. Today, my soul is leaving my body and I am going to leave forever, but all of you are crying for your own sakes and worried about your own future. Nobody is worried about what awaits me." At this moment, the man closed his eyes and died.

Moral:

If we are losing a loved one, we must reassure them of Allāh's ﷻ mercy and make du'ā for them of goodness in the life they are heading towards.

The Soldier and the City

One day, whilst passing the wilderness, a saint came across a soldier who inquired, "Can you please point out to me the way to the city?"

The saint pointed him in the direction of the graveyard. Disappointed by the wrong direction, the soldier came from the graveyard angrily and hit the saint on the head, causing a serious wound. Thereafter, he tied him with a rope and dragged him to the city.

When the people there told him that he had failed to recognise the great saint, the soldier argued, "But he told me the wrong way!"

The saint said, "My son, a town is a place where the population grows everyday. Here, the population is decreasing and the number of graves are increasing. Is not the graveyard really a developing town?" The soldier recognised the saint and fell at his feet.

Moral:
The number of people buried in the graveyards is increasing everyday. Hence, we must never forget them as one day, we will all be heading there. So we must prepare our grave by beautifying them with good deeds.

The Thief and the Gardener

A thief who believed in God's will once broke into a garden and climbed a tree to pick some fruits.

While he was eating the fruits on the branch of the tree, the owner of the garden suddenly appeared and shouted angrily, "Who are you? What are you doing here?"

"A subject of God is on a tree of God and with a hand made by God, is picking and eating the fruits of God," answered the thief.

The gardener made him climb down the tree and tied him to a tree trunk. He then started to beat him with a thick stick. The thief, now in terrible pain, cried out, "Why are you beating me?"

"The stick of God in a hand made by God is striking a subject of God," the gardener answered.

Moral:
We learn from this story that the thief could not get away by trying to steal the fruits from the garden. As Muslims, we should not steal and we should not take something without asking permission from the owner.

Father's Love

Once, for some reason, a king gave orders for a father and his son to be punished, "Tie them to those pillars and give them a hundred strokes with that cane. Start with the father; that would be much better."

The guard said to the father, "Stand still old man. Let me tie you. Now be ready for I'm starting, 1, 2, 3....98, 99, 100."

"All right, that's enough. Now it's the son's turn. Tie him up and beat him," said the king.

"Come boy, stand beside this pillar and give me your hands," said the guard.

"Oh no, please, for God's sake, don't beat my son. Stop beating!" the father pleaded.
"Huh! You endured a hundred strokes without saying so much as a word. But now that your son is being beaten, how is it that you're wailing and weeping?" exclaimed the king.

"The first hundred strokes were not too hard to bear, but these strokes are tearing my heart apart. I can't stand the pain."

Moral:
This story reminds us of how much our parents love us. We must also love our parents and respect them. The holy Prophet 🕌 said, "The pleasure of the Lord is in the pleasure of the father and the displeasure of the Lord is in the displeasure of the father." (Mishkāt)

Follow Your Heart

One beautiful morning, a farmer and his son were taking their donkey to the market to sell it.

The father and his son were walking along together and the donkey was following them. They had not walked far when they passed a group of girls coming from the opposite direction.

"Just look at that," laughed one of the girls, pointing to the farmer. "What foolish people! They walk along the road when they could ride on their donkey!"

The old man quietly told his son to get on the donkey's back and they continued walking towards the market.

Next, they passed a group of men sitting by the side of the road, talking amongst themselves.

"See what I mean?" said one of the men, as the farmer and his son passed by. "The young have no respect for their old parents anymore. Get down you lazy boy and let your father rest his legs!"

The son jumped down from the donkey's back and his father rode on the donkey.

Soon, they came across some women and children.

"Look at the cruel man!" they exclaimed. "He is riding so fast that the poor boy can hardly keep up with him." The farmer stopped and lifted the boy up behind him.

They continued on their way and had almost reached the market when they met a shopkeeper on the road.

"Is that your own donkey?" asked the shopkeeper.

"Yes," replied the farmer.

"Then I am surprised at how you are treating it," said the shopkeeper. "Two people on the back of one donkey is too many. He is sure to die from your strain. You should carry him instead!"

By this time, the farmer was getting used to taking other people's advice. He and his son got off the donkey and tied its legs together. Then, they tied the rope to a long pole and carried the donkey upside down, but their donkey did not want to be carried. Kicking and struggling, the donkey broke the rope holding its feet. It fell into a river near the road and was drowned.

There was nothing the farmer could do except return home. "Next time," said the farmer angrily, "I'll please myself!"

Moral:
Everybody has their own opinion of the right thing to do. We should not follow others' opinions but we should follow our own heart as long as it is pleasing to Allāh ﷻ. That is all that matters in the end.

Three Arms Length for Everyone

Bahlūl liked to visit the graveyards. "People here are good friends," he used to say, "They do not backbite."

Once, he sat in a corner of a graveyard. With a long stick, he started prodding at some of the old skulls which were scattered around.

Hārūn Rashīd, the king, passed by and saw him.

"O Bahlūl! What are you doing?"

"Oh, nothing very important," said Bahlūl, "I am just trying to find out whether the skulls belong to kings or paupers. They are all the same."

"And what is the stick for?" Hārūn asked.

"Well I am measuring the earth," replied Bahlūl.

"Measuring the earth? What are your findings?" Hārūn joked.

"It is one and the same, O king," Bahlūl angrily replied. "Three arm lengths for me, in spite of my poverty and three arm lengths for you, in spite of your pomp and wealth."

Moral:
No matter how rich or poor we are, we will all end up in the earth. Thus, we must always remain humble.

An Intelligent Fisherman

There was a king who was very generous and kind. However, his wife was stingy in nature.

Once, the king went hunting along with the queen and on the way, they stopped by a big tree to rest in its shade. There, an Arab brought a fresh big fish to the king. The king was pleased and gave him 4,000 dīnārs for it.

The queen complained immediately, "This is wasting money. It goes far beyond generosity. You spent 4,000 dīnārs for a single fish! How much would you give away if you were given something more precious? If you paid less than that, you'd be thought inconsiderate and if you wanted to pay more, the treasury would soon be emptied."

She insisted that he had to get the money back from the Arab and pay him the real price for the fish.

"How can I take back what I have already given him? That would not be kingly in manner," exclaimed the king.

"We can trick him and get the money back. We can ask him if the fish is a male or a female. If he says male, we'll immediately say that we were looking for a female and if he says female, we'll say we were looking for a male. This can be the best excuse to give him back the fish and have the money refunded."

"Oh, very well," said the king. He then called the Arab, "You, Arab man, come over here and tell me if this was a male or a female fish."

The clever Arab, who immediately understood the reasoning behind the question, replied, "It was neither, Sir." The king liked his response and ordered that he be given another 4,000 dīnārs.

The man was quite happy to receive another 4,000 dīnārs. When he turned around to leave, he dropped a coin. He bent down and picked it up. The queen took advantage of this to say to the king, "Look how mean he is. He didn't leave a single coin for anybody else."

The king said, "Hey you, come over here again. I gave you thousands of dīnārs but even so, when one of your coins dropped, you bent down and picked that single coin up. Don't you feel ashamed of yourself?"

The man gently replied, "Long live our king. I didn't do it because I'm a stingy person. It's just that the coin bears a picture of your majesty on it and I thought it would be an insult to leave it on the ground to be stepped on by careless people."

The king was so grateful that he granted him another 4,000 dīnārs!

Moral:
Money is to be spent. If we are stingy with our money, we will not gain anything.

Clever Talk

Once, a proud man dismounted from his horse in front of his friend's house to pay him a visit. He saw a boy standing close to his horse and so he said to him, "Hey you lad, come on over here."

"Me?...Yes, Sir," said the boy.

"Come and take hold of the bridle of this horse. Hold on to it until I return from my friend's house."

"But excuse me, Sir, does this horse bite?"
"No, it doesn't."

"How about kicking? Does it kick?"
"Of course not."
"I'm sorry, but may I ask you if it runs away?"
"No, my boy, it doesn't run away either."
"Such a good horse that doesn't bite, kick or run away won't need someone to guard it. Leave it here and let it move around freely and be sure it won't go anywhere."

The boy then turned around and calmly walked away.

Moral:
Sometimes children can be very clever.

The Great Famine

Once, there was a great famine in Madīnah during the

khilāfah (rule) of Sayyidunā Abū Bakr ⬥. Muslims were very worried because all reserves of food and water had finished. Sayyidunā Abū Bakr ⬥ told everyone to pray to Allāh ﷻ for help and be patient.

Sayyidunā Uthmān ⬥ was returning with his caravan from Syria. There were a thousand camels carrying wheat, oil, raisin, food and other merchandise. All the merchants from Madīnah gathered around him. They started putting up their offers to purchase the goods.

One of them said, "I will give you double the profit." Sayyidunā Uthmān ⬥ replied, "I have already been offered more."

Another one said, "Ok, no problem, I will give you four times the profit." Sayyidunā Uthmān ⬥ replied calmly, "I have been offered more than that."

One merchant said, "I will offer you five times the profit, because I know we can sell the goods at a very high price."

Sayyidunā Uthmān ⬥ smilingly said, "But I have already been offered more than that."

All the merchants became shocked. "Who could offer you more than this? All the merchants of Madīnah are here."

"Allāh ﷻ has already promised me at least ten times the profit," replied Sayyidunā Uthmān ؓ and he smiled as he stood up.

"Be my witness. I give out all the camels with goods to the needy people for the pleasure of Allāh ﷻ," Sayyidunā Uthmān ؓ said in a raised voice.

All the worried and needy people received their share and prayed for Sayyidunā Uthmān ؓ.

Moral:
The value of good deeds is much more weightier in the Hereafter than a few pounds in this world.

Promises

Sayyidunā Hudhaifah ؓ and his father Sayyidunā Yamān ؓ

were on their way to Madīnah to meet with the holy Prophet ﷺ when Abū Jahl got hold of them. When he asked them where they were going, they informed him that they intended to meet the holy Prophet ﷺ in Madīnah.

"You are going there to fight against us," Abū Jahl shouted.

When Sayyidunā Hudhaifah ؓ assured him that all they intended to do was meet the holy Prophet ﷺ, Abū Jahl made them promise that they would not fight with the Muslims against him and the other polytheists. Sayyidunā Hudhaifah ؓ was therefore, forced to make the promise.

At that very time, the Muslim army was already leaving for the Battle of Badr and Sayyidunā Hudhaifah ؓ met them on the way.

This was the great battle that Allāh ﷻ refers to as the Day of Furqān (the day when the truth was separated from falsehood). It was the Muslims fighting in this battle who are referred to as the Badriyyīn. They have a very high rank among all of the Sahābah ؓ and the holy Prophet ﷺ stated about them that they were all forgiven by Allāh ﷻ.

When Sayyidunā Hudhaifah ﷺ met the holy Prophet ﷺ, he explained to him that they had been forced by Abū Jahl to promise not to fight in the battle. He had placed a sword to their necks and they had to make the promise to save their lives.

Because their promise was one made under such a threat and not in normal circumstances, Sayyidunā Hudhaifah ﷺ asked the holy Prophet ﷺ to allow them to break their promise, in order to fight with him in the battle.

The holy Prophet ﷺ however, told them that since they had made a promise, they were required to keep it.

At that time, the Muslims needed every man they could get to fight for them because they were so few in number. They were only 313 with just seventy camels, two horses and eight swords. The other Sahābah ﷺ carried only sticks and rocks. However, despite the need for more people, the holy Prophet ﷺ still saw it more important for a person to keep his promise.

Moral:

We learn from this incident that if a promise is made, it

must be kept as far as it is possible. **However, there may be different situations at different times that will not be like this. It is therefore, necessary to always ask the scholars whenever such occasions arise.**

What Answer will I give to Allāh ﷻ?

Sayyidunā Umar ﷜ was the second caliph of Islām and he ruled the Muslim world. Even the emperors of Rome and Persia shivered when they heard his name.

His son, Sayyidunā Abdullāh ﷜, was once travelling somewhere when he became very hungry. There were no restaurants during those days, so when he saw a shepherd with some goats, he thought that he should ask him for some milk to quench his hunger.

"Could you please give me a cup of milk to drink so that my hunger could stop?" he asked the shepherd.

"I don't mind giving you some, but the goats do not belong to me and I have no permission to give you any."

Now, Sayyidunā Abdullāh ؓ was taught by his father, Sayyidunā Umar ؓ who always made sure that all the Muslims of the Muslim Empire were practising on the dīn. He taught his son very well and also taught him wisdom.

Sayyidunā Abdullāh ؓ decided to test the shepherd, so he said, "If you listen to something I have to say, you will benefit very greatly."

"What is it?" the shepherd asked.

Sayyidunā Abdullāh ؓ then explained, "I shall buy one goat from you and give you the money. I shall then have milk to drink and when I wish, I can also slaughter it and have meat. You will then have some money for yourself and if your master asks where the one goat has gone, you may tell him that a wolf ate it."

As soon as he suggested this, the shepherd asked, "Dear man! Then, where is Allāh ﷻ? Where is Allāh ﷻ?"

Sayyidunā Abdullāh ؓ was very happy to hear this and told the shepherd, "As long as there are people like you on Earth, there will always be good and success coming to the ummah."

It is the concern for the Ākhirah (Hereafter) that makes a person alone in a forest realise that Allāh ﷻ is watching and that he will have to answer to Allāh ﷻ for all his actions.

Even though some benefits may be received in this world if people cheat, the fact is that it will all be a big loss for them in the Ākhirah.

Moral:
This story teaches us to be aware of Allāh ﷻ at all times and that we must never spoil our Ākhirah for a little benefit of this world. We must never use people's things without their permission.

Other titles from JKN Publications

A Gift to My Youngsters

This treasure filled book, is a collection of Islamic stories, morals and anecdotes from the life of our beloved Prophet ﷺ, his Companions ﷺ and the pious predecessors. The stories and anecdotes are based on moral and ethical values, which the reader will enjoy sharing with their peers, friends, families and loved ones.

"A Gift to My Youngsters" – is a wonderful gift presented to the readers personally, by the author himself, especially with the youngsters in mind. He has carefully selected stories and anecdotes containing beautiful morals, lessons and valuable knowledge and wisdom.

UK RRP: £5.00

Hadeeth for Beginners

A concise Hadeeth book with various Ahādeeth that relate to basic Ibādāh and moral etiquettes in Islām accessible to a wider readership. Each Hadeeth has been presented with the Arabic text, its translation and commentary to enlighten the reader, its meaning and application in day-to-day life.

UK RRP: £3.00

Du'ā for Beginners

This book contains basic Du'ās which every Muslim should recite on a daily basis. Highly recommended to young children and adults studying at Islamic schools and Madrasahs so that one may cherish the beautiful treasure of supplications of our beloved Prophet ﷺ in one's daily life, which will ultimately bring peace and happiness in both worlds, Inshā-Allāh.

UK RRP: £2.00

How well do you know Islām?

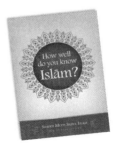

An exciting educational book which contains 300 multiple questions and answers to help you increase your knowledge on Islām! Ideal for the whole family, especially children and adult students to learn new knowledge in an enjoyable way and cherish the treasures of knowledge that you will acquire from this book. A very beneficial tool for educational syllabus.

UK RRP: £3.00

Treasures of the Holy Qur'ān

This book entitled "Treasures of the Holy Qur'ān" has been compiled to create a stronger bond between the Holy Qur'ān and the readers. It mentions the different virtues of Sūrahs and verses from the Holy Qur'ān with the hope that the readers will increase their zeal and enthusiasm to recite and inculcate the teachings of the Holy Qur'ān into their daily lives.

UK RRP: £3.00

Heroes of Islām

"In the narratives there is certainly a lesson for people of intelligence (understanding)." (12:111)

A fine blend of Islamic personalities who have been recognised for leaving a lasting mark in the hearts and minds of people.

A distinguishing feature of this book is that the author has selected not only some of the most world and historically famous renowned scholars but also these lesser known and a few who have simply left behind a valuable piece of advice to their nearest and dearest.   **UK RRP: £5.00**

Marriage - A Complete Solution

Islām regards marriage as a great act of worship. This book has been designed to provide the fundamental teachings and guidelines of all what relates to the marital life in a simplified English language. It encapsulates in a nutshell all the marriage laws mentioned in many of the main reference books in order to facilitate their understanding and implementation.

UK RRP: £5.00

Gift to my Sisters

A thought provoking compilation of very interesting articles including real life stories of pious predecessors, imaginative illustrations and much more. All designed to influence and motivate mothers, sisters, wives and daughters towards an ideal Islamic lifestyle. A lifestyle referred to by our Creator, Allāh ﷻ in the Holy Qur'ān as the means to salvation and ultimate success.

UK RRP: £6.00

Gift to my Brothers

A thought provoking compilation of very interesting articles including real life stories of pious predecessors, imaginative illustrations, medical advices on intoxicants and rehabilitation and much more. All designed to influence and motivate fathers, brothers, husbands and sons towards an ideal Islamic lifestyle. A lifestyle referred to by our Creator, Allāh ﷻ in the Holy Qur'ān as the means to salvation and ultimate success.

UK RRP: £5.00

Arabic Grammar for Beginners

This book is a study of Arabic Grammar based on the subject of Nahw (Syntax) in a simplified English format. If a student studies this book thoroughly, he/she will develop a very good foundation in this field, Inshā-Allāh. Many books have been written on this subject in various languages such as Arabic, Persian and Urdu. However, in this day and age there is a growing demand for this subject to be available in English .

UK RRP: £3.00

Ideal Youth

This book contains articles gathered from various social media avenues; magazines, emails, WhatsApp and telegram messages that provide useful tips of advice for those who have the zeal to learn and consider changing their negative habits and behavior and become better Muslims to set a positive trend for the next generation. **UK RRP:£4:00**

Ideal Teacher

This book contains abundance of precious advices for the Ulamā who are in the teaching profession. It serves to present Islamic ethical principles of teaching and to remind every teacher of their moral duties towards their students. This book will Inshā-Allāh prove to be beneficial for newly graduates and scholars wanting to utilize their knowledge through teaching. **UK RRP:£4:00**

Ideal Student

This book is a guide for all students of knowledge in achieving the excellent qualities of becoming an ideal student. It contains precious advices, anecdotes of our pious predecessors and tips in developing good morals as a student. Good morals is vital for seeking knowledge. A must for all students if they want to develop their Islamic Knowledge. **UK RRP:£4:00**

Advice for the Students of Knowledge

Allāh ﷻ describes divine knowledge in the Holy Qur'ān as a 'Light'. Amongst the qualities of light are purity and guidance. The Holy Prophet ﷺ has clearly explained this concept in many blessed Ahādeeth and has also taught us many supplications in which we ask for beneficial knowledge.

This book is a golden tool for every sincere student of knowledge wishing to mould his/her character and engrain those correct qualities in order to be worthy of receiving the great gift of Ilm from Allāh ﷻ.   **UK RRP: £3.00**

Pearls of Luqmān

This book is a comprehensive commentary of Sūrah Luqmān, written beautifully by Shaykh Mufti Saiful Islām. It offers the reader with an enquiring mind, abundance of advice, guidance, counselling and wisdom.

The reader will be enlightened by many wonderful topics and anecdotes mentioned in this book, which will create a greater understanding of the Holy Qur'ān and its wisdom. The book highlights some of the wise sayings and words of advice Luqmān ﷷ gave to his son.

UK RRP: £3.00